Foreword

United Press has long encouraged young people to get involved in poetry. For over a decade we have produced free books featuring poetry written by children at various schools. By donating a large number of copies (50 or more) of these books to each school we have not only helped them to raise valuable funds but we have also given their pupils an outlet which has encouraged them to get involved in poetry.

Throughout this period we have also included a lot of young people in anthologies along with adult poets.

Every young poet under 16 has been given a free copy of any anthology which includes their work. There's no doubt that this kind of encouragement has helped a lot of young poets take those first vital steps towards getting recognised for their talents.

This book is the result and also the extension of that process. Most of the poets featured in it have one thing in common - besides the fact that they stand out as young writers who have a great gift for expressing themselves. They are writers who have had work published by us over the past few years. Many of them have had several poems published in our anthologies and have received free copies of all of them.

We decided to produce this book to help each one of our nineteen "Young Poet Laureates" gain further recognition for their talents and help them to progress in their artistic achievement. I'm sure the poetry world will hear a lot more of them.

Peter Quinn, Editor

Contents

The poets who have contributed to this volume are
listed below, along with the relevant page upon
which their work can be found.

ABBIE MAGUIRE
(Born 1995)

*From a very young age,
Abbie has been enthused
by everything that hap-
pens in her life and the
lives of those closest to
her. Her English teach-
ers and family have
always encouraged her
long-lived passion for
reading and writing.
Sharing sentiments with
others is, to her, the true beauty of writing.*

A WHISPER IS A SCREAM IN A SILENT CROWD

A whisper is a scream in a silent crowd,
Hidden in a dark and dreamless kind of world.
Beneath the hollow veneer is the bitter taste of
despair.
Cocooned in by a smile when rain stops in midair.

Secrets burst at their seams but only what we allow,
A whisper is a scream in a silent crowd.
Ribbons of grey cross unclouded sky,
Like celestial heaven burned by hell's fire.

My eyes suddenly open from the thoughts in my

brain,
I try, in musky light, to tell myself I'm sane.
A whisper is a scream in a silent crowd,
A shout, full of power, never a sough.

Someone's white knuckled fingers clutch my neck,
I announce in a rasp: I have no regrets.
After all these years it's solemnly avowed,
A whisper is a scream in a silent crowd.

THE WISP OF A MEMORY

Nestling in the under-banks of darkness lies a rose,
I watch its colour fade as the petals start to close.
The icy splinters of winter are piercing through the clouds,
Everything lies pulverised, hidden under a shroud.

Tears smash on the ground and cracks start to meet,
I always see your face in strangers on the street.
Lamp posts are shadowed by the chilling moonrise,
I collapse on the concrete but no one hears my cries.

I am captured by the shadows, in an imaginary light,
And the asylum where I sleep; it haunts me at night.
And now you say our past lies in amicable air,
But beneath the noxious veneer, lies the taste of despair.

I am poisoned by my persistence, laced with torture,
I breathe a little closer, a little stronger, a little longer.

CONFESSION

Deep in the crevasses of my confounded mind,
Lies a bed of roses spread out by time.
Even with two glasses of the finest wine,
That clinquant stars can never quite align.
When time's winged chariot comes to us to serve,
We could walk on broken glass with nothing to preserve.
I could fall through the cracks or be consumed in shadows,
He tries to shoot to the stars with bent and broken arrows.
We yearned for sunshine but had to live in the rain,
And instead of compromise, he chose disdain.
Our love story is frayed with one fragment to spare,
But I can't let him go, he's like a drug, I swear.

CALLUM BRASSINGTON
(Born 1996)

Callum was born in Derbyshire. He first came into poetry after hearing about a competition in the local press, and soon discovered he enjoyed it. His work is influenced by real life, and his style is non-fiction and straight to the point. His other interests include football, tennis, reading, drama, and taking part in the Duke of Edinburgh Award scheme.

A SPRINKLE OF SNOW

Snow is falling
And sticks to the ground
Sprinkles from the sky
It lands all around

A white sheet-like cover
What a beautiful sight
Nothing when it's dark
But covered in light

It comes in the winter
Rarely in spring
It brings out the festivities

Makes the children all sing

It comes down for Christmas
Brings a 'gosh' and a 'phew'
Laying on the streets, all around us
Creating a magnificent view

MESSAGE IN A BOTTLE

The swishing of the seas
Is music in your ears,
Like the sound of taps
Releasing tiny tears.
It bobs upon the surface
Travelling with the waves,
But inside that glass bottle
The paper there is saved.
The message comes towards your
Bouncing to your hands,
Eventually it slows down
Landing in the sands.
The bottle then is opened
To find paper inside,
That just came from an unknown place
Bobbing on the tide.

EASTER CELEBRATIONS

Easter Sunday is the time
When Jesus rose again
After all that suffering

On a cross that gave him pain

Now Easter resembles
New season and new born
When plants and trees are growing
To replace the old and worn

Eggs are now presented
As the outside shows the tomb
Inside represents new life
That comes from in the womb

WILLIAM AND KATE

From the future to the past
A royal engagement is here at last.
Kate and Wills will get married,
Pride across Britain being carried.

29th of April is the date
When Prince William will marry Kate.
Westminster Abbey is where it will be,
With hundreds and thousands there to see.

Prince Charles will be attending,
As well as the Queen.
The country on standstill,
To show what it means.

How proud would Diana be
To see the service, them lawfully wed,
With them looking forward
to their future ahead?

EMILY KATHARINE BUTTON
(Born 2000)

Emily lives in Edmonton, North London. Emily started writing at a very young age and is influenced by her powerful imagination and all the poems and stories she has read. In her spare time, she re-enacts scenes from the Roman and Napoleonic periods.

THE RACE

My heart is pounding in my chest,
My legs and arms are aching,
My head is in a spin,
All I can see is nothingness,
Blurs everywhere I look,
Everything is fuzzy,
I can hear shouts and screams,
Laughs and cries.
I must keep moving,
I must go on,
I have made it, I have won.
I am the champion of the race!

THE TRAVELLER'S LOVE

My love is the road, the path and the open sky.
The breeze that blows through my hair.
My love is the sea, the birds, the ocean and the day.
My love is the sunset at dusk,
With all its radiant beauty,
All the colours imaginable,
Shiny and iridescent, all magnificent in their own glittering way.
I am the traveller,
And this is my love.

SPACE

I lie on my back
On the cool, green grass,
And look up to the sky,
I see millions of stars,
Planets and constellations,
I find …
The big dipper,
Orion and his magnificent belt,
The northern star,
And many more …
I see a comet passing!
I make a wish …
I wish that one day,
I can join the stars and planets,
And be …
An astronaut.

DARKNESS

Thick darkness surrounds me,
It goes where it likes,
Covering everything it can find.
It crawls all over me,
Grabbing and pulling at me,
Tugging and teasing me,
Laughing as I struggle,
No light,
What was that?
I heard a noise,
It's like footsteps,
It's coming closer,
Oh help,
I wish I would stop quivering
I hide under the blanket,
I get ready to scream …

Then Mum turns on the light,
Phew, it was only Mum,
I am safe …
For now!

ELLEN MALARKEY
(Born 2001)

Ellen was born in Preston and now lives in Chorley. She loves reading and her ambition is to be a writer or an actress. She finds inspiration by sitting outside in the garden or by watching people and their actions.

FRIENDS

When I've had a fall out,
And I don't care,
I feel so lonely and sad
But you're always there.

It doesn't matter if
You're near or far
If we're separated
By miles
When I need cheering up
You always make me
Smile.

CHRISTMAS EVE

It's very exciting on Christmas Eve
But when it's Christmas dinner,

It's always a heave!
Everyone pushes to get their food
If I don't get any roast potatoes,
I'll be in a mood!

THE OPTICIANS

The day we went to the Opticians,
We had a big surprise.
It was raining cats and dogs,
Cows, sheep and hogs,
But Mum didn't blink an eye.
The reason we found was …
That she needed some glasses!

ALONE

I come here to be alone
It's wonderful on my own.
The birds tweeting all around,
Making the most beautiful sound.
The leaves fluttering in the breeze
Everything's so peaceful,
Even the bees.

However when it's time to go,
I feel a little sad inside
But in my soul I really know
I'll return another time.

MEG DENHAM
(Born 1997)

Meg was born in Banbury. She started writing at the age of 5, and is influenced by the experiences she has and poets like Ted Hughes. She has written lots of short stories, and loves writing poetry because she can write about her interests and express her feelings. Her hobbies include horse riding, drumming and playing the guitar, and her ambition is to be an equine vet.

MUSIC

It's a personal choice,
Some like rap and some like rock.
It's a personal choice,
Some like classical and some like jazz.

It's an influenced choice,
Some friends don't care and some are persuasive.
It's an influenced choice,
Some parents nag and some don't mind.

It's a mood changing choice,
Some are sad and some are happy.
It's a mood changing choice,
Some are funny and some are bizarre.

It's a changing choice,
Some days pop and some days blues.
It's a changing choice,
Some days hip hop and some days dance.

It's a personal choice,
Some like rap and some like rock.
It's a personal choice,
Some like classical and some like jazz.

FLORENCE

Big and magnificent,
Great like an elephant.
A giant in disguise,
With huge trusting eyes.

Her glorious mane,
Would put a lion to shame.
Her beautiful nose,
Smells just like a rose.

Her massive round hooves,
Ensure that she moves.
Her flickering ears,
Would reduce a tough man to tears.

Her tail is so long,
To dislike it would be wrong.
She is very slow,
I love her anyway though.

Big and magnificent,
Great like an elephant.
A giant in disguise,
With huge trusting eyes.

JACK CARLE CARNEGIE
(Born 2000)

Jack was born in London and he currently lives in Bexhill-On-Sea. He is a lover of animals and considers himself a Wiccan, appreciating all that nature has to offer. He loves nothing more than sharing his ideas and experiences in writing.

PARALLEL UNIVERSE

If sparrows were protected,
And leopards roamed at night,
And ice-cream men played jazz-rock songs,
Could black mosquitoes bite?

When you go out for a sidewalk ride,
And park away from yellow lines,
And come back to see a sea-blue card,
Could jam be kept inside a jar?

And if you're in a parallel world,
Away from where trees grow roots way up high,
Could cakes really be made with eggs and bicarb?
My best friend asks, peering down at the sky.

RAGNAROK

Asgard lies in ashes
Fenrir at the gates
The Midgard Serpent thrashes
While Loki's men await
The signal from their master
To tidal wave Vio'arr
And the army's silhouette
Ragnarok's final war
Lif and fair Lifthrasir
In among the leaves
As Esir and God, Odin,
Their anger starts to seethe
And out of Greek Asphodel
And of Greek Tartarus
Begins to come Arkantos,
Ajax, Odysseus
While they arrive, they bring the siege
That broke the gates of Troy
Colossi and the Sirens
To Ragnarok's high deploy

SEWING THE AUSTRALIS

In and out and in and out the colours leap and swirl,
Round about and upside-down the brightness bends
and curls,
The brassy scarlet indigo in shades of midnight green,
The grassy, pearly navy blue and twists of never seen,
Burnt burgundy, majestic mauve and berceuse

threaded blue,
The colours of wallpaper white, cream parchment, old and new,
All flowing free in dusty mist,
Insistent colours, ones that insist,
The low down, earthy brown of night,
The sea green-blue, oh what a sight!
The needles of colour, the needles of light,
Sew in and out and in and out colours that leap and swirl,
Round about and upside-down the thread it bends and curls!

NOT WHAT IT SEEMS

The silver falls of coconut streams
Lapping silver, flowered dreams
Upon the pure rock icy shore
Of what could chances take once more
And feel the wind of breezy seams
Wash ashore the petal streams
Through trees of orange sunlight beams
And shows all is not what it seems

The lights of aurora
Reflect the trees
In waters of endless, silver dreams
And reveal of what could be once more
Glides of hope from the anvil of Thor
But in the midst of minty dreams
Cleansed rocks of life are endless, see

And shows all is not what it seems

Twisting branches
Opal leaves
Full in bloom
The tall, proud trees
In the pattern of nature's weave
And shows all is not what it seems

The light of night
And the dark of day
Glide along like suns to say
Rippling feelings
Moons of white
Show that all four winds at night
Or in the day like suns, to say
Rippling feelings shower this day

COURTNEY MILLS
(Born 1998)

Courtney was born in Wakefield and now lives in a village just outside of Perth, Scotland. She first started writing poems when she was 9 years old, and since then, she has had several poems published.

THINGS THAT MAKE ME SATISFIED!

Music and reading are a lot of fun,
Bathing and getting a tan in the sun,
Having a bath and watching soaps,
Going on holiday and riding on boats,
Admiring my sparkly glitzy ring,
These are a few of my favourite things.

NATURE

I stand outside in the wintry air around,
The snowflakes drift across the moor,
Laying a soft white blanket over my surrounds,
Bringing happiness to everyone,
Winter time is here,
Wrap up warm and enjoy this time of year.

I look here, I look there, and I look everywhere,
Nature is what I see,
Sheep milking their baby lambs,

Cows giving birth to baby calves,
As spring draws to a close,
Here I was, as close to nature as I could be.
Another time of joyfulness throughout another joyful
year.

As the sun shines high,
We all smile wide,
Yet another time of year,
Summer is here,
Looking far in front the sea sparkles,
The beach is full of happiness as cheerful families
gather.

Standing high up on a mountain top,
Looking from left, to right, in all directions,
Beautiful surroundings there they lay
Tall trees shedding their autumn leaves,
Autumn air blows around me.
Another year has come to its end,
Time for the nature cycle to start over again.

STREAMS …

Streams, streams,
Go with the flow,
Streams, streams,
Go like the winds blow,
Streams, streams,
Purl around the city park,
Streams, streams,

Cascade over the mountain tops,
Past a stark,
Streams, streams,
Go with the flow.

AUTUMN

Tall trees swaying,
As the chittery wind that blows.
The old and wrinkly leaves
Falling off the trees and dying.
Rain pouring from the sky
Like water running in a bath.
Small birds tweeting,
The red squirrels gather the golden acorns fallen.
The spiky hedgehog snuffling to find shelter,
As the heavy fog falls,
And the warm sun leaves.
Waking up in the morning,
To find our car windows all white and icy.
Coming home from work
To find it all cold and dark outside.
Time to go to sleep and for our nice autumn rest.

CAITLIN LAMMIN
(Born 1996)

Caitlin lives in Hertfordshire. She writes short stories and poetry and has always had a passion for words. Her other hobbies include acting and singing, as well as Kenjutsu, the Japanese martial art of sword fighting.

LADDER TO THE SKY

Hand over hand,
Rung over rung,
Climbing, always climbing,
Until the climbing's done.

Up to the sky,
The cloudy blue,
I'll climb forever,
To get to you.

I miss you so,
I have to be there,
Up to the heavens,
The dead man's lair.
My love for you,

Burning strong,
Someday I will reach you,
It won't be long.

MISSING YOU

All the seasons I will wait,
Sitting under the tree we met,
Surrounded by the still waters,
That watched us while we kissed,
All the elements rage around me,
All around me while I wait,
The sun, the moon and stars,
All take turns to watch me,
Watch me wait for you,
Until I'm old and grey,
Until the day I can't go on,
On the day I die,
Not a moment I will rue,
And I shall whisper into the wind
'I miss you.'

I KNOW THE PIECES FIT BECAUSE I WATCHED
THEM FALL AWAY

I know the pieces fit because I watched them fall
away,
I know there is a picture because I saw it the other
day,
I know there is an answer there because I have found
it there before,

But now it's got me wondering if there is one anymore.

I thought I knew the answer on a time so long ago,
But it seems that it has altered as the broken times will
show,
And now my life is empty and I feel like punching
hell,
No one even knew you 'cos I never kiss and tell.

Broken swirling hatred
But there is love there too
A love through shattered pieces
Broken pictures
Lost answers.

Yes.
I still love you.

JACK FRUIT

He walked slowly past my window,
His garb was all coloured green,
His collar was high, his brow was low,
The strangest sight I've seen.

He wore a crown of berries and leaves,
And anklets of cherry stones,
Strawberry stems were sewn up his sleeves,
But his skin clung to his bones.

Apples and bananas were tied onto his back,
Pears were what his feet rested on,
He turned to face me, his eyes deep black,
And then Jack Fruit was gone.

EMILY WOODBERRY
(Born 1996)

*Emily was born in
Wolverhampton and has
aspirations for great things -
becoming a widely-enjoyed
poet being one of them. She
is most commonly described
as 'experimental', and
always tries to put her own
personal experiences and
imaginative details into
every line.*

KARMA

Innocent until framed guilty,
Revenge tastes sour on the receiving end,
Growing into a skin of regret never to shed.

No nostrum can save you now,
This engram fossilised during your periods of igno-
rance,
You can't brush over the consequences.

The ripples will ring around the source
of disturbance on their pure tranquillity,
Don't mistake a pebble for a stone.
Like a fly in a web,
There is no escaping,

You can't delay reality any longer.

Like a red rag to a bull,
You shouldn't snort around so casually,
'Over my dead body.'

Like the venom of a snake,
They'll assist in your descent
with the truth behind your 'probity.'

ONE HORSE RACE

So many connotations at midnight,
I succeeded in stealing your voice,
Pressed against your chest,
Tearing away your words.

A part of you I can still feel close to,
Let the doors slam shut,
Close up for the night,
Escape into a reclusive suburbia …

Stood at the station,
Where the train will never stop,
My ticket has expired,
My paper heart wears thin.

Everything you say under lock and key,
Dead to you by tomorrow,
But in my mind, a stuck record -
'C-c-c-cut it out!'

Your sweet melody forms the smoothest undercoat,
An instrumental without structure, without finish,
Without me,
Let me be your voice.

THE WONDERS OF LOVE!

Slipping through the net,
Blinking reality through my
Reluctant dream,
A lie so kind,
A truth so untold.

As vivid as nightmare,
With all the odds of
A perfect world,
Collapsing into my mind,
Into your arms.

As I orbit around my imagination gone wild,
Tempting and beautiful and
Soft to the touch,
So defended from logic,
So defenceless to my heart.

Each syllable of Irish wine,
Trickling down the perfect body
Of the glass,
Delicate and graceful,
Fragile and weak.

Enter my dimension,
Clear my air don't
Fog the class,
A new silhouette reflected,
In your extraneous tears.
THE EDITOR

A symphony unwound,
Into strings and valves,
Nuts and bolts of the clockwork on which we run,
Doesn't this all sound familiar?

Commercially pure:
Heart bleeding the truth.
On the skip in the baseline we'll fall into place,
Will you be brave and stand against?

Hold the print.
Stop the press.
A new muse on the horizon …

EMILY JOYCE
(Born 1997)

Emily was born in Rutland and has lived on a farm all her life. Writing poetry helps her to relax whilst studying for exams, and she hopes to, one day, have a book of her own published, becoming an inspiration to the young authors of future generations.

TIMELESS BEAUTY

I gaze out to the horizon,
And one thing I can see;
One thing that's nothing,
But the great blue sea.

Timeless beauty is captured,
In this soft rolling water,
An elegance possessed
By no mother or daughter.

For if our Lord had
Succeeded in only one way,
He made the waves sound
Magical, throughout night and day.

And as the tide carries me further,

Towards where I must go,
I feel the earth is performing
My own special show.
The air around me feels cool,
And the stars look so bright,
And the water seems so calm,
As I venture through the night.

And as the sun wakes up,
The world's imagination does too.
Except nothing is around me,
But the ocean blue.

A timeless beauty is the sea,
A natural wonder like no other,
A taken for granted treasure,
That costs nothing to discover.

A CHILD'S PRAYER

Matthew, Mark, Luke and John,
Bless the bed that I lay on.
And before I lay down to sleep
Please give my soul to Christ to keep,
Because the world brings round a new day,
I ask you gentlemen that as I pray;
May you watch over my family and friends,
And shower them with good fortune until the end,
May my schooling career be bonny and well,
With my life in your hands, it shall be swell.
So John, Luke, Matthew and Mark,

Please guide me through this eve of dark.

FLANDERS FIELDS
*a version of the original poem 'In Flanders Fields' by John
McCrae*

In Flanders fields the hero's rest,
Row upon monumental row;
A duvet of earth drapes over bodies,
Upon which, red poppies grow.
Only a cross now marks their passion,
A will to fight for life,
These warriors always battled on,
Throughout each woe and strife.

I am the dead and you are too;
We once saw such skies of blue,
But now we sleep forever more;
In Flanders fields.

Bear no malice to countries past
For very short days ago,
We lived to hear sweet birds' song,
We watched a lonely sunset glow.
If ye listen through the noise,
You can still hear
The silence of fear and murder blow;
Above Flanders fields.

So let us bind hands together
And unite as one;

For the dead are still living
And dream to live on.
Light a torch, wave it up high;
For the poppies still grow;
In Flanders fields.

CHLOE HALMKAN
(Born 1998)

Chloe was born in Reading. She enjoys art, drama and poetry, or anything else that is creative, and has just started learning Ninjitsu. Chloe gets her inspiration for her poetry from what she sees around her and how she feels. Her ambition is to be a poet and publisher.

RIVER NILE

I am a wise, old man
I don't sleep
Yet I dream of the past
When I was a young lad

I used to spin, swirl, swish and shine
I used to pirouette with power
As I paced myself past the forest and the land
Twirl, twist and turn as I engulf stones and leaves

Yet I am cursed
I can travel through the land
But cursed to the same land
No change
No freedom
I am lonely
With only the sun and moon for company

People say I have a gift
To live a thousand of years upon end
But I can't even change
Because still I'm stuck, in-between a bank
No help at all

PEER PRESSURE

Peer pressure is easy to do
It squeezes you deep inside
Until you feel sick
And a shiver goes down your back

As your friends chant on and on
I dare you
Come on, are you a chicken?
Your head begins to swirl
You have to fight the urge to keep in control
Before your life eases to a stop
And you do something that scars you for life

IN THE SKY

What's that in the sky?
It looks like a plane
No, a superhero
Oh, it's just a bird

A giant bird
With dazzling beauty
It reflects my past

My younger days
It shows my cringes
And my wonder
The moments of truth
And the moments of lies

I think once more
Is this my life
Or someone else's?

The radiant colours
Can be seen through the sky
It blinds me
Though I can see

I remember the day
When it gave me the choice
The choice of freedom
To die free

MEGAN AUDREY BLAKE
(Born 1998)

*Megan lives in Sunderland.
She started entering poetry
competitions about eighteen
months ago and has had five
poems published to date. She
would love to be a famous
author one day.*

I SEE AND SAY NOTHING

They said your heart was made of stone,
You said your country was your throne,
Your clothes were black, your hair was red,
A face so white, as though dead.
What a ruler you turned out to be,
Certainly the best of the Tudor dynasty,
Your father Henry had such power,
Unfortunately he sent your mother to the tower.
Very soon she had no head,
Because of your birth she was sent to her deathbed.
Virgin Queen hereditary was left for us all to see,
Yours was the greatest victory in English history,
Defeat of the Armada in 1588,
Made you monarch with much debate.
Westminster Abbey is where you lie,
A place for your people to say goodbye,
If we could speak together today,
I would certainly know the words you would say,
'video et taceo'.

42

THE SIREN

The voice that cried throughout the night,
The voice that said follow the light,
The voice that laughed as the ship went down,
The voice that mocked the sobs from the town,
The voice that sang like a nightingale,
The voice that moved waves like the force of a whale,
The voice that shouted, 'look at me,'
The voice that took sailors to the depths of the sea,
The voice that came from a world below,
The voice that echoed a deathly hallow,
The voice that's beauty beyond compare,
The voice that said, 'look at me, if you dare!'

WHAT A WONDERFUL WORLD

Morning song brings along the beauty of the day,
The clouds up in the sky move along in such a dreamy
way,
Rising sun across the shore as the waves kiss goodbye to
the sand once more,
Spring and summer go by so fast,
If only the warm sunshine was here to last,
Soon winter comes and with it snow,
Small children playing their faces all aglow,
Don't forget autumn and the nip in the air,
With piles of leaves blowing everywhere,
The seasons pass and the years go by,
New generations are born,

And old ones die,
The circle of life goes round and round,
Like a carousel moving off the ground,
What a wonderful world we live in each day,
So please cherish your life in a very special way ...

BEHIND THE WALL

I'm invisible to the human eye ...
The rumours, the vicious lies,
Why this talking behind my back?
Like a stuck radio track.

Shall I name them, you may ask?
These awful girls from my past,
They used to want me, but now don't talk,
Little sniggers and off they walk.

Nowhere to run, nowhere to hide,
What has happened to my pride?
Like a rabbit, scared by a fox,
Wanting to disappear inside a box.

Someone help me I want to shout,
But there's always too many of them about,
On and on like a ticking clock,
Large waves lashing against a rock.

This is my message to you this day,
Please don't destroy another life this way,
Three young girls without a heart,
Managed to tear my wonderful world apart ...

JESSIE WHICHELOW
(Born 1997)

*Jessie was born in St Helier
Hospital and now lives in Merton
Park. She has been writing for
about 8 years, and her ambition in
life is to become a journalist, writing books and poetry in her spare
time.*

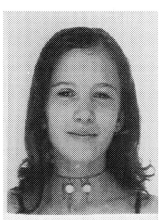

THE VIEW

Sitting on top of Albury hill,
Everything so quiet and still,
Apart from the wind, blowing a gale,
Following, following, a never ending trail.

The leaves all turning, look like a rug,
Fields of green and paths are dug,
A farmhouse small, and quite alone,
Farmer and farmer's wife, walking home.

Clouds like castles pretty and white,
All look lovely from this height,
Oh this lovely Albury hill,
Everything so quiet and still.

THE RIVERS OF LOVE

When the rivers of love flow through your life,
When the vicar pronounces you husband and wife,

When whole streams of happiness flow through your heart,
When you feel that nothing can bring you apart,
When you sing with the stars, floating high and above,
That's when you know that you're truly in love.

IN THE MIDST OF MY CHILDHOOD

Beyond the rugged wall of roses,
Beyond the rotting wooden fence,
Beyond the weeds all running wild,
A rundown house, a lonely child.

Beyond the bush of dying holly,
Beyond the wilting willow tree,
Beyond the birds, so calm and mild,
A rundown house, a lonely child.

Beyond the flashing lights and sirens,
Beyond the stifled cries of pain,
Beyond the sheets, so high they're piled,
A crying mum, a dying child.

Beyond the icy, rigid pathways,
Beyond the trees so bare and cold,
An empty house, so sad and bleak,
And memories that make you weep.

ORIANNE BREAKSPEAR
(Born 2001)

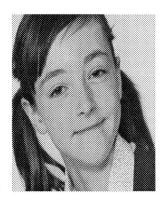

Orianne was born in Buckinghamshire and now lives in Great Missenden in the beautiful Chiltern Hills. She has always loved reading and writing poems, and particularly enjoys poetry as so much can be conveyed in so few words.

THE SECRET GIRL

I searched for you so desperately
I searched for you so longingly.
But here you are one plain girl
With matching dowdy clothes.
But maybe inside that shell of yours
You're hiding something rare.
But neither of us have the courage to speak
So for now, we'll both just stare.

TRICKED

Deep, dark tiger's eye, shadowed
Glares.
Receives spit of fire
Summons all within
More than expected, suffers
Silence …
Opponent ready slithers, scales like spikes

A scratch and a claw
A yelp and a cry
Pain, staggers forward
Both caught. Tricked
If they had the chance they never would again.

BEAUTY

The piercing screech struck terror
The messenger lay distraught
Disaster gathered, fell like rain on kingdoms near and
far.
Though black eyed Beauty shone
'Twas evident at first
But when the command of royalty sang
'Twas covered up once more
The lack of time was desperate
Was claimed a needy cause
But secret was not kept well, and Beauty screeched
Once more

NEW SEASON

After a break again, all of nature reunites
It's every wonder marching side by side
Walking the world in unison
All jumbled up but it seems familiar
They change everything until almost nothing is the
same
Within a few weeks the new leaders are in full stride
But soon enough, you know it's going to change
again …

48

JOSHUA ETESON
(Born 1995)

*Joshua lives in Dewsbury and
has been writing poetry for
seven years. He writes poetry
as a means of expressing
himself and has had poems
published in 6 books so far.*

HAUNTED

There sits a grey school upon a hill
and in that school there is a lifeless hall
and in that very hall you will find
nothing to be seen, absolutely nothing at all.

The spider webs decorate the hall
to signify that no one has been there
lifeless students walk down the corridors
the shadows following them, being the only one who
cares.

The days grow colder and darker each hour
as the calling of death grows near
but no one hears her silent screams
as the shadows beckon her closer, telling her there is
nothing to fear.

The school sits empty as shadows play
the rain falling down making the unknown real

her life was never known, her last breath taken
no one ever knew how the shadows could feel.
No one goes near, in fear of the forces that be
dancing and singing to their own songs of pain
reflections of lives past before them
listening to the soft cries of the rain.

Some call it ghosts, the shadows that play
reflections of the life they lived before
they walk around from place to place
never able to leave the heavy wooden doors.

THE BEGINNING OF THE END

It isn't the words but the silence that speaks,
It isn't the laughter but tender whispers that I hear,
Beauty lies not in the face but the soul and spirit,
This is when I hear the wind whistling
This is when I see the specks of dust
Dancing like the gypsy queen
I feel not the thought but the emotion within,
I feel not the sorrow but the joy of sacrifice,

It's just the beautiful beginning to a mournful end,
The end that will part from soul to spirit,
And song from dance,
The end that will part the wind from dust
And shatter the silence,
It comes gracefully and showers the tears,

There is time still;
For it is only the beginning,
Of a long and winding journey
To the other side;
The other chapter of my life

EILIDH FERGUSSON
(Born 1995)

Eilidh lives in the northwest of Lancashire. She likes writing and reading almost anything, and she is trying to be a Buddhist, though finding it difficult. Her favourite subject is science, because it is so interesting.

ELEMENTAL

Narrator: Not in Ice and not in Fire,
             The spark of Life, the heart's desire

Ice: Slow and deadly,
             Ice will win.
             Pride is no object.
             I am indestructible,
             Last forever, failing never.
             I live without Life.

Fire: Fear me, I burn.
             Dare touch me, I bite.
             My pride is above all.
             I, the deadly killer, strike.
             Ice shall go, I will live on.
             Untouchable, am I.

Sprit: I flee between the enemies.

52

Unknown in all,
Life in essence.
But death shall befall.
To never live and never die,
To freeze forever or burn ferociously.

Narrator: Of these to choose, Ice or Fire,
Which one? Choose or Nonexist.

STEPHANIE CLAYTON
(Born 1995)

Stephanie started to write poetry when she was 13 years old. She likes to write about things very close to her, with people around her providing limitless inspiration. Her other hobbies include writing prose, scripts, and swimming.

FAIRYTALE WEDDING

You look into my eyes and say
'You wanted all that fairytale stuff?'
I smile at the old cliché.
Thinking, 'As long as you're there, it's enough.'

'Every little girl wants that,' I reply.
'But I'm not a little girl anymore.'
You take my hand and I start to fly,
I've never felt less unsure.

So, you say, 'I do,'
And my heart jumps.
Well, 'I do,' too,
And my heart still thumps.

You're my husband. I'm your wife.
That's all that ever mattered.

54

We're together, for all my life,
Together, our love is treasured.

My fairytale dream came true,
The day I met you.

I'M LOST

I'm lost.
A year ago you took my hand,
And together we flew over this land.
You looked me in the eye,
And swore you'd never make me cry.

I'm lost.
A year had passed now,
Together all this time, how?
But now you're leaving me,
Through my tears I cannot see.

I'm lost.
Never make someone your everything;
Cos when they're gone you have nothing.
We still talk every day.
But now I don't know what to say.

I'm lost.
You're coming home for Christmas;
You hold me tight and we kiss.
I've missed you,
But you're back, now we're starting anew.

But before long you're leaving again; for school,
I'm lost without you. I'm lost.

UNIVERSITY

University.
Now you've got to leave me,
I knew the day would come
Very soon, yet now I'm numb,
Even from our very first day,
Reality was drifting, taking me away,
So now I'm falling, falling fast;
I wish I could live in the past.
Today you leave, to start your school,
You promise that everyday you'll call.

University.
New things to see.
I'm younger than you, I've always known; but your
Voice seems so far away, behind a brand new door.
Everyday you've got something new to say,
Rain or snow, we talk every day.
So now it's time, you're coming home,
I won't have to feel alone.
Today you got back to town,
You came straight to me, turned my frown upside
down.

University.
Now the holiday's over, time for you to go back.
I'll miss you, but I know you're always coming back.

£1,000 to the winner

All top poets never miss sending an annual entry for the National Poetry Anthology. Over 250 winners are selected every year, each one representing a different UK town. All winners are published in the National Poetry Anthology and all receive a free copy of the book. Many of these poets have never been published before. Send up to THREE poems (on any subject) up to 20 lines and 160 words each, by the annual closing date of **June 30th**
to -
United Press Ltd Admail 3735, London EC1B 1JB
Tel 0844 800 9177
www.unitedpress.co.uk
One overall winner also receives a cheque for £1,000 and the
National Poetry Champion Trophy.
Even if you've won previously, and had your poetry published in it, this free competition is always open to you. And as it's the only big free poetry competition of its kind, it's the first you should put on your list to enter.

Another £1,000 to be won

A poem about someone or something from your home town can win you a top prize in this annual competition.

Anyone can submit up to three poems for the competition. The top poem will win £1,000 cash. There is no age limit and no entry fee.

"The poem can be about something or someone from the poet's home area," explained United Press Publications Director, Peter Quinn.

"It can be descriptive, historic, romantic, political, or personal - anything you like, as long as there is some local connection.

This competition is open to anyone and is completely free to enter - so what have you got to lose?"

Send up to THREE poems, up to 20 lines and 160 words each, by the annual closing date of December 31st, to the above address.

Welcome to the Short Story Society

Even if you have never had any prose published before, you should submit something to the Short Story Society.

It's the perfect platform for your writing talents and gives you a fantastic opportunity to get your work published. Our aim is to help writers to create short stories and get them published and appreciated.
There's no membership fee to join the Society.
To be a member you must submit a short story. You must then have that story accepted by us. If we do accept it, we will publish it in a compilation of short stories by several authors and give you five copies of the book.

We will also put your story on our website at shortstorysociety.co.uk for visitors to read and enjoy - in the months leading up to the publication of the finished book. We will also give you 40 per cent discount if you want to produce your own book. Having a short story published is a wonderful and inspirational learning process for all authors - especially those who have never had their prose published before.

Your next step is to submit a short story. It could be handwritten or it could be typewritten. It could be on email or any kind of disc. You should send it to:
The Short Story Society
United Press Ltd
Admail 3735 London EC1B 1JB
www.shortstorysociety.co.uk
email - info@shortstorysociety.co.uk
phone - 0844 800 9177.
Your story can be on any subject.
It can be aimed at children, it can be a ghost story, it can be a love story, a horror story, a true life story.